# The Cat
# Came Back

by Frances Ann Ladd

Illustrated by Duendes del Sur

™

SCHOLASTIC INC.

New York   Toronto   London   Auckland   Sydney
Mexico City   New Delhi   Hong Kong   Buenos Aires

Scooby-Doo
sat on his mat.
The black
and orange cat
hissed at him.

Then the cat ran off.
Scooby ran after the cat.
But that cat was fast.

*Crash!*
Scooby landed in a ditch!
The cat came back.

Scooby ran
after the cat again.
Scooby did not see
Shaggy.
*Bam!*
Scooby ran
right into him!
The cat came back.

Shaggy packed
a picnic basket.
The cat hid in the basket.

Scooby lifted the lid.
The cat sat inside!
The cat purred.
Scooby wagged his tail.
This cat was not so bad.

Scooby gave the cat
a dish of milk.
The cat licked up
all the milk
in the dish.

Then she licked Scooby!
A cat kiss!
Scooby and the cat
can be pals!